KS2
9–10
Years

Master Maths at Home

Extra Challenges

Scan the QR code to help your child's learning at home.

mastermathsathome.com

How to use this book

Maths — No Problem! created **Master Maths at Home** to help children develop fluency in the subject and a rich understanding of core concepts.

Key features of the Master Maths at Home books include:

- Carefully designed lessons that provide structure, but also allow flexibility in how they're used.

- Speech bubbles containing content designed to spark diverse conversations, with many discussion points that don't have obvious 'right' or 'wrong' answers.

- Rich illustrations that will guide children to a discussion of shapes and units of measurement, allowing them to make connections to the wider world around them.

- Exercises that allow a flexible approach and can be adapted to suit any child's cognitive or functional ability.

- Clearly laid-out pages that encourage children to practise a range of higher-order skills.

- A community of friendly and relatable characters who introduce each lesson and come along as your child progresses through the series.

You can see more guidance on how to use these books at **mastermathsathome.com**.

We're excited to share all the ways you can learn maths!

Copyright © 2022 Maths — No Problem!

Maths — No Problem!
mastermathsathome.com
www.mathsnoproblem.com
hello@mathsnoproblem.com

First published in Great Britain in 2022 by
Dorling Kindersley Limited
One Embassy Gardens, 8 Viaduct Gardens, London SW11 7BW
A Penguin Random House Company

The authorised representative in the EEA is Dorling Kindersley
Verlag GmbH. Arnulfstr. 124, 80636 Munich, Germany

10 9 8 7 6 5 4 3 2 1
001–327102–May/22

This book was made with Forest Stewardship Council™ certified paper - one small step in DK's commitment to a sustainable future. For more information go to www.dk.com/our-green-pledge

All rights reserved. Without limiting the rights under the copyright reserved above, no part of this publication may be reproduced, stored in, or introduced into a retrieval system, or transmitted, in any form, or by any means (electronic, mechanical, photocopying, recording, or otherwise), without the prior written permission of the copyright owner.

A CIP catalogue record for this book is available from the British Library.

ISBN: 978-0-24153-946-0
Printed and bound in the UK

For the curious
www.dk.com

Acknowledgements

The publisher would like to thank the authors and consultants Andy Psarianos, Judy Hornigold, Adam Gifford and Dr Anne Hermanson.

The Castledown typeface has been used with permission from the Colophon Foundry.

Contents

	Page
Numbers to 1 000 000	4
Adding and subtracting	6
Factors and multiples	8
Prime numbers	10
Multiplying 3-digit numbers	12
Dividing 4-digit numbers	14
Adding and subtracting fractions	16
Multiplying fractions	18
Multiplying mixed numbers	20
Ordering and comparing decimals	22
Adding and subtracting decimals	24
Percentages	28
Line graphs	30
Capacity	34
Perimeter	36
Area	38
Angles	40
Position	44
Answers	46

Ruby   Elliott   Amira   Charles   Lulu   Sam   Oak   Holly   Ravi   Emma   Jacob   Hannah

Numbers to 1 000 000

Lesson 1

Starter

Jacob is making numbers using digit cards.
This is the last number he makes.

| 2 | 1 | 6 | 9 | 3 | 4 |

He then decides to swap the places of some digit cards and makes 3 swaps.
What is the greatest number he can make?
What is the smallest number he can make?

Example

To make the greatest number we need to have as many hundred thousands, ten thousands and thousands as possible.

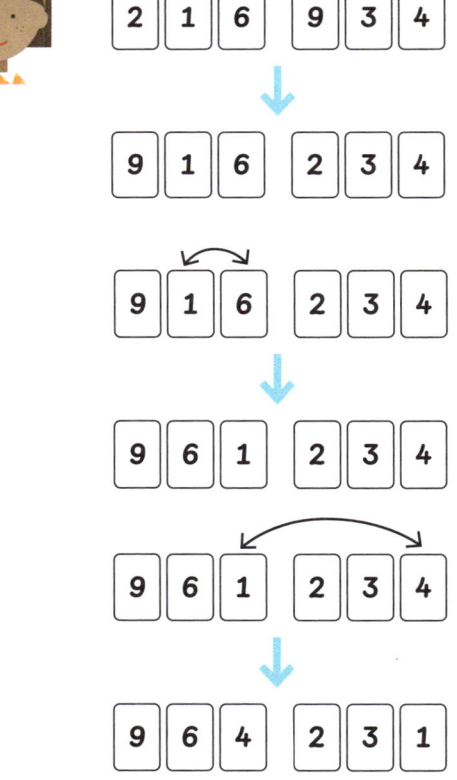

The greatest digit is 9.

The second greatest digit is 6.

The last digit we can change should be 4.

964 231 is the greatest number Jacob can make by making 3 swaps.

	2	1	6	9	3	4
Change 1	1	2	6	9	3	4
Change 2	1	2	3	9	6	4
Change 3	1	2	3	4	6	9

To make the smallest number we place the 1 in the hundred thousands place.

123 469 is the smallest number Jacob can make by making 3 swaps.

Practice

1 Swap the places of 2 digits in each number with 2 others to make a number as close as possible to 500 000.

(a) 328 045 →

(b) 429 375 →

(c) 743 021 →

(d) 521 997 →

2 Use the following digits to make the number closest to:

| 7 | 2 | 3 | 5 | 2 | 3 |

(a) 200 000 →

(b) 350 000 →

(c) 490 000 →

Adding and subtracting

Lesson 2

Starter

Emma and her family are on holiday in Indonesia. Emma has Rp1 000 000 (Indonesian Rupiah) to spend (approximately £50).

Rp375 659

Rp240 999

How much will she have left after buying the 2 items?

Example

Start by finding the cost of the 2 items.

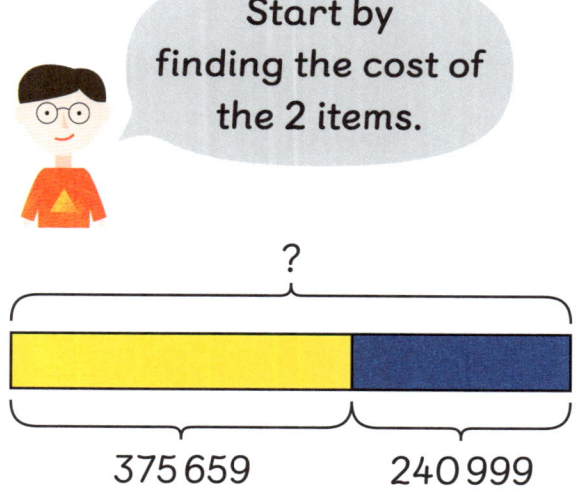

$$\begin{array}{r} {}^13\,7\,{}^15\,\,{}^16\,{}^15\,9 \\ +\,2\,4\,0\,\,\,9\,9\,9 \\ \hline 6\,1\,6\,\,\,6\,5\,8 \end{array}$$

375 659 + 240 999 = 616 658

The total cost of the 2 items is Rp616 658.

6

Subtract the total cost of the 2 items from the amount Emma started with.

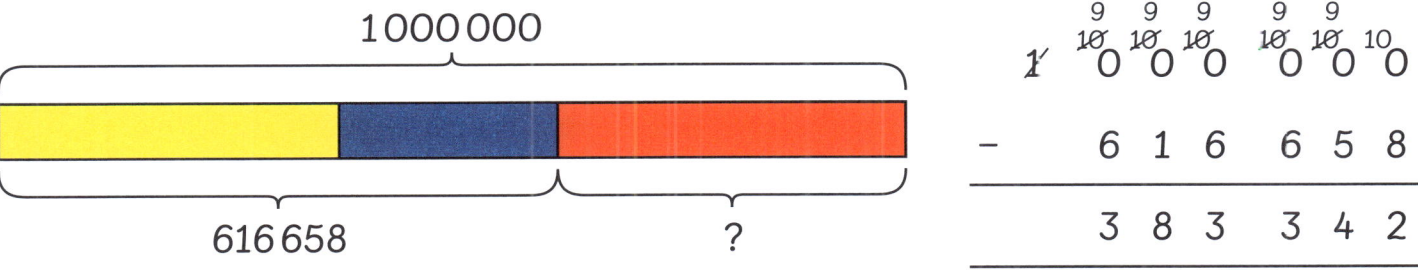

1 000 000 − 616 658 = 383 342

Emma will have Rp383 342 left after buying the 2 items.

Practice

Emma's dad buys the following items.
How much money will he have left if he starts with Rp1 000 000?

Rp482 199

Rp337 805

Emma's dad will have Rp ☐ left.

Factors and multiples

Lesson 3

Starter

A group of pupils take part in 3 outdoor activities: kayaking, climbing and archery. They are put into groups of 4 for kayaking, groups of 8 for climbing and groups of 14 for archery. Each activity has more than 1 group.

What is the minimum number of pupils taking part in the outdoor activities?

Example

What is the smallest number divisible by 4 and 8?

$8 \div 4 = 2$ $8 \div 8 = 1$

8 is the lowest common multiple of 4 and 8.

We know that each activity has more than 1 group so climbing must have more than 8 pupils.

Find the multiples of 4 and 8.

Multiples of 4: 4, 8, 12, 16, 20, 24, 28, 32, 36, 40, 44, 48, 52, 56
Multiples of 8: 8, 16, 24, 32, 40, 48, 56

There may be 16 pupils. Four groups of 4 pupils kayaking.
Two groups of 8 pupils climbing.

 Is 16 a multiple of 14?

 Find the multiples of 14.

Multiples of 14: 14, 28, 42, 56, 70

56 is the smallest number that is a multiple of 4, 8 and 16.

 We can say that 56 is the lowest common multiple of 4, 8 and 16.

The minimum number of pupils taking part in the 3 outdoor activities is 56.

 We can also say that 4, 8 and 14 are common factors of 56.

Factors of 56: 1, 2, 4, 7, 8, 14, 28, 56

Practice

 1 A baker makes some doughnuts. He can pack them all exactly into boxes of 6. He can also pack them all exactly into boxes of 8 or 18 without having any doughnuts left over.

(a) What is the minimum number of doughnuts the baker has made?

(b) Using the minimum number of doughnuts the baker has made, what other size boxes could the baker pack the doughnuts into without having any left over?

Prime numbers

Lesson 4

Starter

Oak looked at her maths homework and noticed something.

10 = 1 × 10   11 = 1 × 11   12 = 1 × 12   13 = 1 × 13
10 = 2 × 5   12 = 2 × 6
                              12 = 3 × 4

What do you think she noticed?

Example

All of the even numbers in Oak's list have more than 2 factors.

Is it true that all even numbers have more than 2 factors?

$2 = 1 × 2$

2 is the only even number that is also a prime number.

All multiples of 2, greater than 2, have more than 2 factors. Look at these examples.

20 = 1 × 20   56 = 1 × 56   102 = 1 × 102
20 = 2 × 10   56 = 2 × 28   102 = 2 × 51
20 = 4 × 5   56 = 4 × 14   102 = 3 × 34
                   56 = 7 × 8   102 = 6 × 17

Numbers with more than 2 factors are called composite numbers.

21 = 1 × 21   35 = 1 × 35   99 = 1 × 99
21 = 3 × 7   35 = 5 × 7   99 = 3 × 33
                                  99 = 9 × 11

21, 35 and 99 are **composite numbers**.

A prime number has only 2 factors, 1 and itself.

1 is not a prime or a composite number as it only has 1 factor.

Practice

1 Fill the table using the following numbers.

32   14   63   29   43   15   148   117   101   105   144

Composite numbers	Prime numbers

2 List all the odd composite numbers between 70 and 100.

11

Multiplying 3-digit numbers

Lesson 5

Starter

The Fresh Supermarket receives a delivery of 346 boxes, each containing 24 teabags. The Sunshine Supermarket receives a delivery of 692 boxes, each containing 12 teabags. Is Hannah correct?

"I think each supermarket receives the same number of teabags."

Example

"Start by multiplying 692 by 12."

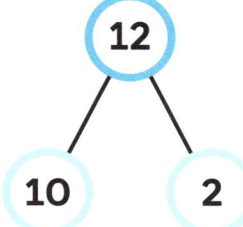

$692 \times 10 = 6920$
$692 \times 2 = 1384$
$692 \times 12 = 8304$

```
      ¹6  9  2
   ×      1  2
   ─────────────
    1  3  8  4   →  692 ×  2 = 1384
    6  9  2  0   →  692 × 10 = 6920
   ─────────────
    8  3  0  4   →  692 × 12 = 8304
```

$700 + 700 = 1400$
$1400 - 16 = 1384$

"Multiply 346 by 24."

```
         ¹3  ¹²4  6
   ×          2   4
   ─────────────────
       1  3   8   4   →  346 ×  4 = 1384
       6  9   2   0   →  346 × 20 = 6920
   ─────────────────
       8  3   0   4   →  346 × 24 = 8304
```

> 692 is double 346.
> 12 is half of 24.

> 692 × 12 and 346 × 24 have the same product.

Hannah is correct.

Both supermarkets receive the same number of teabags.

Practice

1. What do you notice about the products of 235 × 28 and 470 × 14?

```
      2  3  5              4  7  0
  ×      2  8          ×      1  4
     ┌──┬──┬──┬──┐        ┌──┬──┬──┬──┐
     │  │  │  │  │        │  │  │  │  │
     └──┴──┴──┴──┘        └──┴──┴──┴──┘
  +  ┌──┬──┬──┬──┐     +  ┌──┬──┬──┬──┐
     │  │  │  │  │        │  │  │  │  │
     └──┴──┴──┴──┘        └──┴──┴──┴──┘
     ┌──┬──┬──┬──┐        ┌──┬──┬──┬──┐
     │  │  │  │  │        │  │  │  │  │
     └──┴──┴──┴──┘        └──┴──┴──┴──┘
```

2. Match the expressions with the same value.

139 × 24	•	•	132 × 36
456 × 30	•	•	278 × 12
264 × 18	•	•	742 × 14
371 × 28	•	•	912 × 15
214 × 14	•	•	76 × 16
152 × 8	•	•	428 × 7

Dividing 4-digit numbers

Lesson 6

Starter

A truck makes 4 return journeys between Brighton and Edinburgh in a week. The total distance the truck travels over the 4 return journeys is 6048 km. What is the distance between Brighton and Edinburgh?

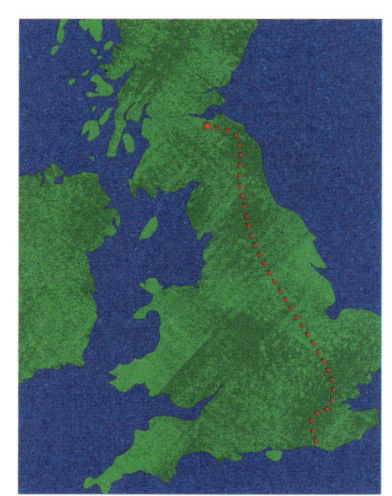

Example

Four return journeys is the same distance as 8 one-way journeys.

Divide 6048 by 8 using long or short division.

```
        7  5  6
8 ) 6  0  4  8
  - 5  6
    ─────────
       4  4  8
    -  4  0
    ─────────
          4  8
       -  4  8
       ─────────
             0
```

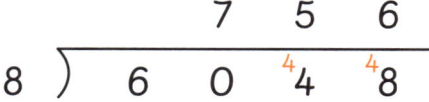

6048 ÷ 8 = 756

The distance between Brighton and Edinburgh is 756 km.

Practice

1 A bus makes 3 return journeys between Plymouth and Newcastle.
The total distance the bus travels over the 3 return journeys is 4122 km.
What is the distance between Plymouth and Newcastle?

The distance between Plymouth and Newcastle is ☐ km.

2 The distance between London and Mumbai (India) is 8 times the distance between Paris (France) and Genoa (Italy). The distance between London and Mumbai is 7184 km.
What is the distance between Paris and Genoa?

The distance between Paris and Genoa is ☐ km.

Adding and subtracting fractions

Lesson 7

Starter

Holly makes some chocolate milk by mixing $\frac{1}{20}$ l of chocolate syrup with $\frac{7}{10}$ l of milk. She trips as she walks to the table, spilling $\frac{1}{4}$ l of her chocolate milk.

What is the volume of the chocolate milk Holly has left in her jug?

Example

Make the denominators the same so the fractions can be added.

We can't make twentieths into tenths here.

$$\frac{7}{10} \xrightarrow{\times 2} \frac{14}{20}$$

We need to make tenths into twentieths.

$$\frac{1}{20} + \frac{7}{10} = \frac{1}{20} + \frac{14}{20}$$
$$= \frac{15}{20}$$

The volume of Holly's chocolate milk before she spilt it was $\frac{15}{20}$ l.

 We need to subtract $\frac{1}{4}$ l from $\frac{15}{20}$ l.

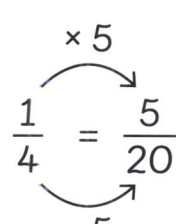

 The denominators need to be the same to subtract.

$\frac{15}{20} - \frac{1}{4} = \frac{15}{20} - \frac{5}{20} = \frac{10}{20}$

Holly has $\frac{10}{20}$ l or $\frac{1}{2}$ l of chocolate milk left in her jug.

Practice

1 Ravi mixes $\frac{1}{2}$ l of yellow paint with $\frac{1}{8}$ l of blue paint to make light green paint. He uses $\frac{1}{4}$ l on his painting. What is the volume of paint that Ravi has left?

Ravi has $\frac{\Box}{\Box}$ l of paint left.

2 Ruby makes a tropical punch using $\frac{3}{4}$ l of orange juice and $\frac{1}{12}$ l of lime juice. She gives $\frac{1}{3}$ l of the tropical punch to her sister and keeps the rest for herself. What volume of tropical punch does Ruby keep for herself?

Ruby keeps ☐ l of the tropical punch for herself.

17

Multiplying fractions

Lesson 8

Starter

Hannah cuts 3 different types of sushi rolls into 6 equal pieces.
She takes 1 piece from each of the different sushi rolls.
How much of the sushi rolls are left altogether?

Example

Each roll has 5 sixths.

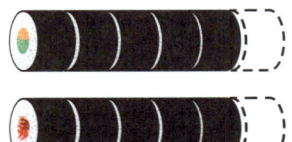

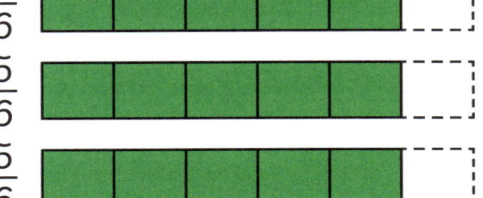

$3 \times \dfrac{5}{6} = \dfrac{15}{6}$

The denominator, sixths, names the size of the fraction. The numerator tells us how many we have.

$\dfrac{15}{6} = 2\dfrac{3}{6}$

We have 3 groups of 5.

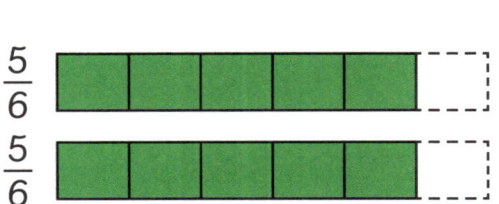

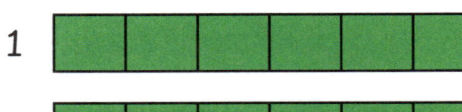

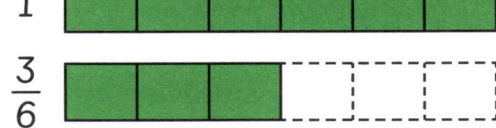

There are $2\dfrac{3}{6}$ sushi rolls left altogether.

Practice

1 Oak has 3 chocolate bars. Each bar is the same size and has 8 equal pieces. If Oak takes 1 piece from each bar, what is the total number of chocolate bars she has left?

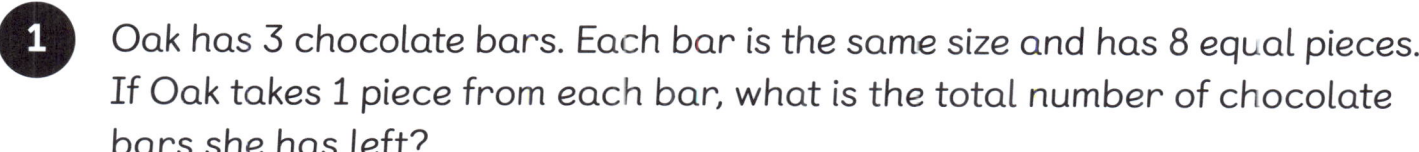

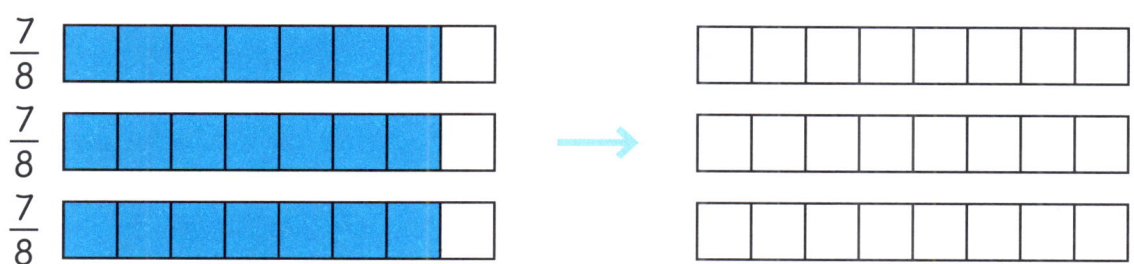

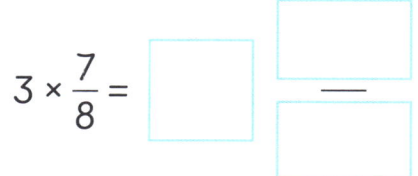

$3 \times \dfrac{7}{8} = \boxed{} \dfrac{\boxed{}}{\boxed{}}$

Oak has $\boxed{} \dfrac{\boxed{}}{\boxed{}}$ chocolate bars left.

2 Charles uses $\dfrac{7}{10}$ l of water, $\dfrac{7}{10}$ l of vegetable stock, $\dfrac{7}{10}$ l of chicken stock and $\dfrac{7}{10}$ l of coconut milk to make soup.

What is the total volume of soup that he makes?

The total volume of soup Charles makes is $\boxed{} \dfrac{\boxed{}}{\boxed{}}$ l.

Multiplying mixed numbers

Lesson 9

Starter

The mass of a rabbit is 2 kg.
The mass of a small dog is $3\frac{3}{4}$ times greater than the mass of the rabbit.
What is the mass of the dog?

Example

We can multiply the whole numbers and the fraction.

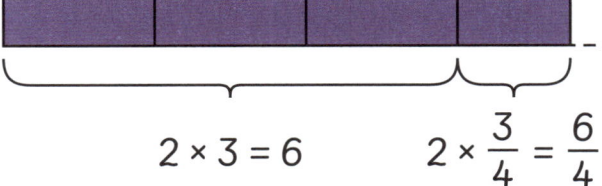

$2 \times 3 = 6$
$2 \times \frac{3}{4} = \frac{6}{4}$

$2 \times 3\frac{3}{4} = 6\frac{6}{4}$
$= 7\frac{2}{4}$

$\frac{6}{4} = 1\frac{2}{4}$

I know $\frac{2}{4}$ is equal to $\frac{1}{2}$.

The mass of the dog is $7\frac{1}{2}$ kg.

Practice

1 A restaurant offers cheesecake or chocolate cake for dessert. The restaurant has 2 chocolate cakes. It has $2\frac{4}{5}$ times more cheesecake than chocolate cake. How many cheesecakes does the restaurant have?

The restaurant has ☐ $\frac{☐}{☐}$ cheesecakes.

2 Sam uses 3 l of water to water his front garden. He uses $5\frac{5}{8}$ times more water to water the back garden.

(a) What volume of water does Sam use to water the back garden?

Sam uses ☐ $\frac{☐}{☐}$ l of water to water the back garden.

(b) How much water does he use in total?

Sam uses ☐ $\frac{☐}{☐}$ l of water in total.

Ordering and comparing decimals

Lesson 10

Starter

The following volumes of paint will be mixed to create a unique colour.

1.3 l   1.24 l   1.301 l

How can we compare the volume of each paint colour?

Example

We can show each number using place-value counters.

1.3   = 1 0.1 0.1 0.1

1.24 = 1 0.1 0.1 0.01 0.01 0.01 0.01

1.301 = 1 0.1 0.1 0.1 0.001

1.2 is less than 1.3. We do not need to look beyond the tenths to find the smallest value.

1.24 l < 1.3 l
1.24 l < 1.301 l
1.24 l is the smallest volume of paint.

1.3 and 1.301 have the same number of ones and tenths.

1.301 is $\frac{1}{1000}$ greater than 1.3.

1.3 l < 1.301 l

We can put the volumes of paint in order from smallest to greatest.

1.24 l   1.3 l   1.301 l

smallest ⟶ greatest

Practice

1 Use >, < or = to fill in the blanks.

(a) 3.44 ☐ 3.05   (b) 4.99 ☐ 5.01

(c) 2.564 ☐ 2.645   (d) 34.014 ☐ 34.01

(e) 5.679 ☐ 5.08   (f) 6.1 ☐ 6.099

2 Put the following numbers in order from smallest to greatest.

smallest ⟶ greatest

(a) 3.4, 3.5, 3.42

(b) 9.08, 9.131, 9.12

(c) 13.021, 13.101, 13.001

3 Put the masses in order from greatest to smallest.

4.039 kg   4.307 kg   4.35 kg

greatest ⟶ smallest

Adding and subtracting decimals

Lesson 11

Starter

On Monday Ravi had 1.25 l of orange juice and 1.155 l of apple juice in his fridge. By Wednesday Ravi had drunk 1.5 l of juice. What is the total volume of juice Ravi has remaining in his fridge?

Example

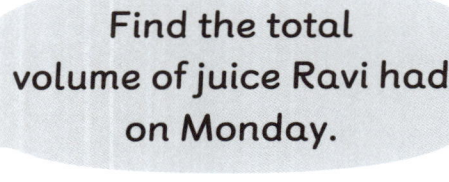
Find the total volume of juice Ravi had on Monday.

Start by adding the thousandths.

1.25 = 1.250

```
   1 . 2 5 0
 + 1 . 1 5 5
 ───────────
         . 5
```

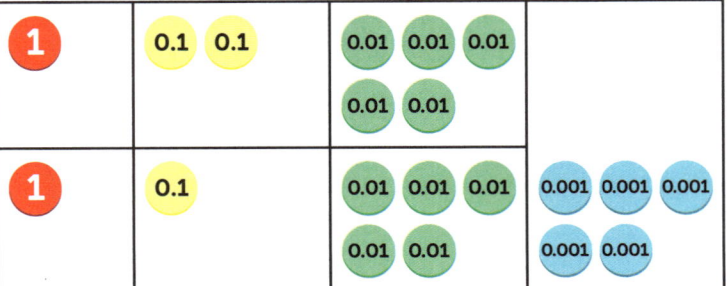

Add the hundredths.
5 hundredths + 5 hundredths = 10 hundredths

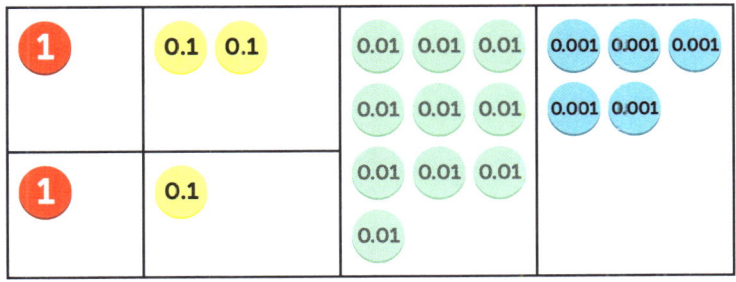

Rename 10 hundredths as 1 tenth.

10 hundredths = 1 tenth

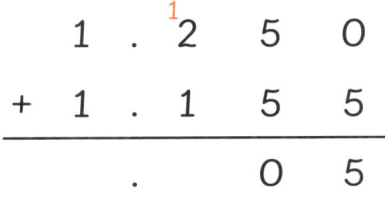

$$\begin{array}{r}1.\overset{1}{2}5\,0\\+\ 1.1\,5\,5\\\hline .\ \ \ 0\,5\end{array}$$

Add the tenths.

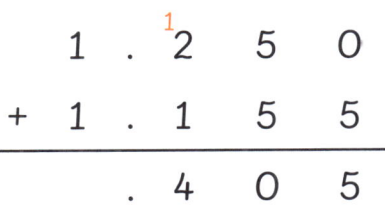

$$\begin{array}{r}1.\overset{1}{2}5\,0\\+\ 1.1\,5\,5\\\hline .\ 4\,0\,5\end{array}$$

Add the ones.

$$\begin{array}{r}1.\overset{1}{2}5\,0\\+\ 1.1\,5\,5\\\hline 2.4\,0\,5\end{array}$$

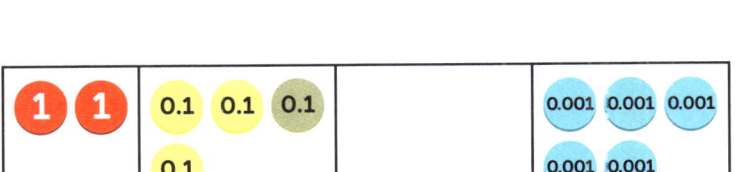

Ravi had 2.405 l of juice on Monday.

 Subtract 1.5 l from 2.405 l to find the volume of juice remaining.

 We are not subtracting any hundredths or thousandths.

```
  2 . 4 0 5
- 1 . 5
_____
      0 5
```

There are not enough tenths.

 Rename 1 one as 10 tenths.

```
  2 . 4 0 5
- 1 . 5
_____
    . 0 5
```

```
  ¹2̸ . ¹⁴4̸ 0 5
-  1 . 5
_____
       . 9 0 5
```

Subtract the ones.

```
  ¹2̸ . ¹⁴4̸ 0 5
-  1 . 5
_____
    0 . 9 0 5
```

 We use 0 to show there are no whole numbers.

Ravi has 0.905 l of juice remaining in his fridge.

Practice

1 Hannah mixed 2.34 kg of soil and 2.155 kg of pebbles to use for her plants. She used 1.7 kg of the mixture for her pot plants.

(a) Find the total mass of the mixture.

2.34 kg + 2.155 kg = ☐ kg

The total mass of the mixture is ☐ kg.

(b) Find the mass of mixture remaining once Hannah has used 1.7 kg.

☐ kg − 1.7 kg = ☐ kg

The mass of the remaining mixture is ☐ kg.

2 Ruby and her sister are making bracelets. Ruby cuts 4.6 m of thread from a 9 m piece and gives it to her sister. She then buys a 5.55 m piece of thread. What is the total length of thread Ruby has now?

Ruby has ☐ m of thread.

Percentages

Lesson 12

Starter

The table shows the number of goals scored by each football team in a single season.
How can we find the percentage of goals each football team scored out of the total of 300 goals scored in the season?

Team	Number of goals
Greystone Greats	30
Hills United	75
Plymouth Pirates	18
Waterside United	60
Tunbridge Tigers	57
Brighton Bosses	39
East Coast Flyers	21
All teams	300

Example

Percentage means how many out of 100.

The table shows the number of goals out of 300.

The Greystone Greats scored 30 out of the total of 300 goals.

We need to find how many this is out of 100.

$$\frac{30}{300} \overset{\div 3}{\underset{\div 3}{=}} \frac{10}{100}$$

$\frac{10}{100} = 10\%$

The Greystone Greats scored 10% of the total goals scored in the season.

 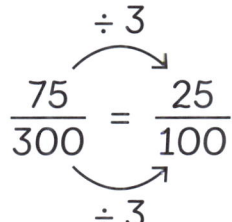 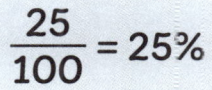 

What percentage of the total goals did Hills United score?

$$\frac{75}{300} = \frac{25}{100}$$ (÷ 3)

$$\frac{25}{100} = 25\%$$

Practice

1 The table shows the number of goals scored by each football team out of the total of 300 goals scored by all teams in the season.
Complete the table.

Team	Number of goals	Percentage of the total of 300 goals
Greystone Greats	30	10%
Hills United	75	25%
Plymouth Pirates	18	
Waterside United	60	
Tunbridge Tigers	57	
Brighton Bosses	39	
East Coast Flyers	21	

2 Four friends played a card game. The table shows the number of bonus points scored by each friend out of the maximum possible bonus points available for each player.
Complete the table.

Name	Maximum number of bonus points	Bonus points scored	Percentage of maximum bonus points scored
Charles	40	10	
Holly	25	15	
Ravi	30	18	
Lulu	70	49	

Line graphs

Lesson 13

Starter

The graph shows the distance a bus travelled over a period of time. How can we describe the journey the bus made?

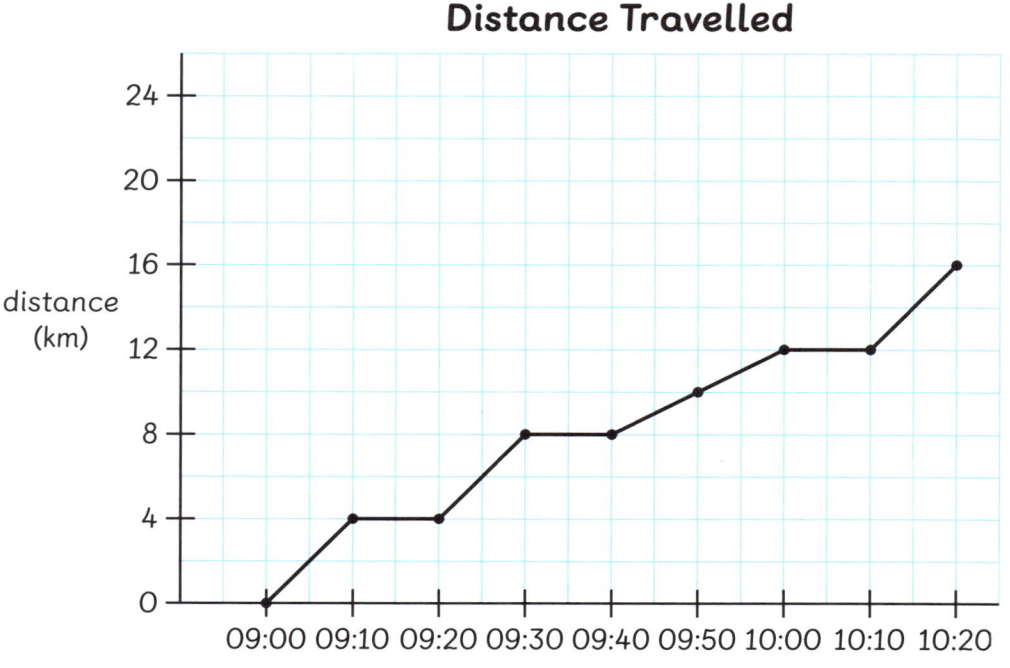

Example

For how many minutes was the bus travelling at a rate of 4 km every 10 minutes?

We can see that the bus travelled at a rate of 4 km every 10 minutes for 30 minutes.

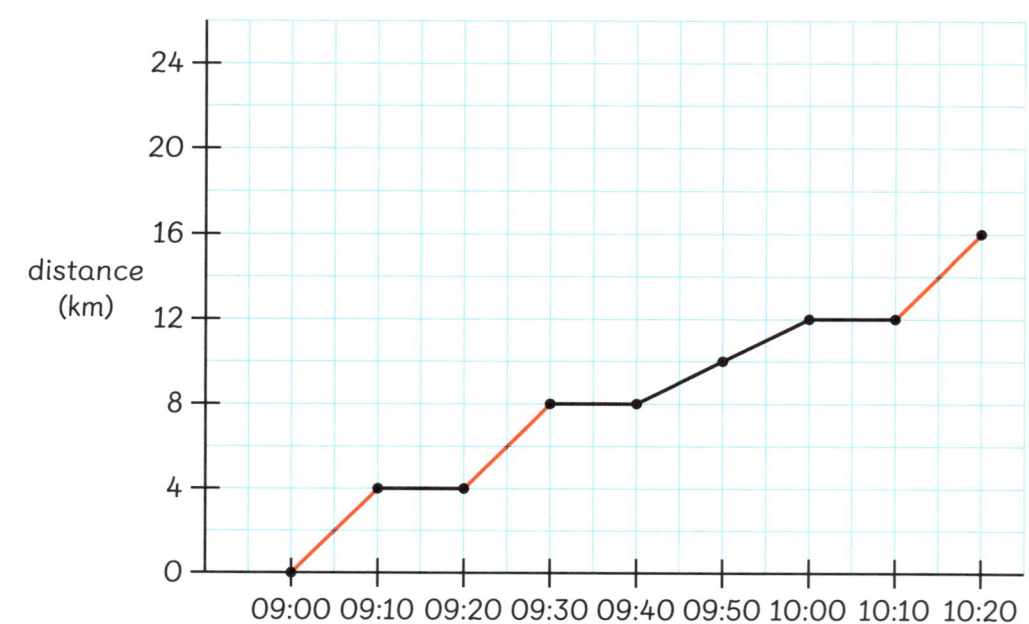

30

 How many times did the bus stop?

 The bus stopped 3 times.

 The bus stopped for a total of 30 minutes.

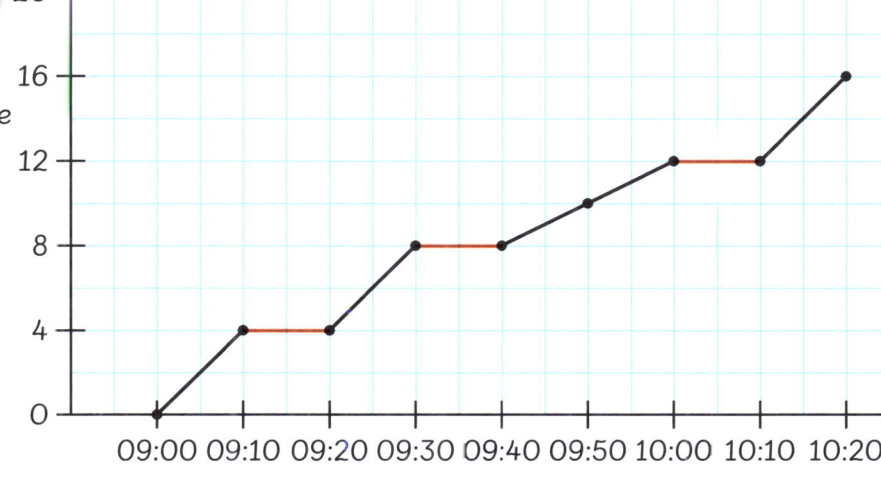

 At one point in the journey, the bus slowed down because of traffic. When was that?

 Between 09:40 and 10:00 the bus travelled at a rate of 2 km every 10 minutes.

 This is slower than the other times the bus was moving.

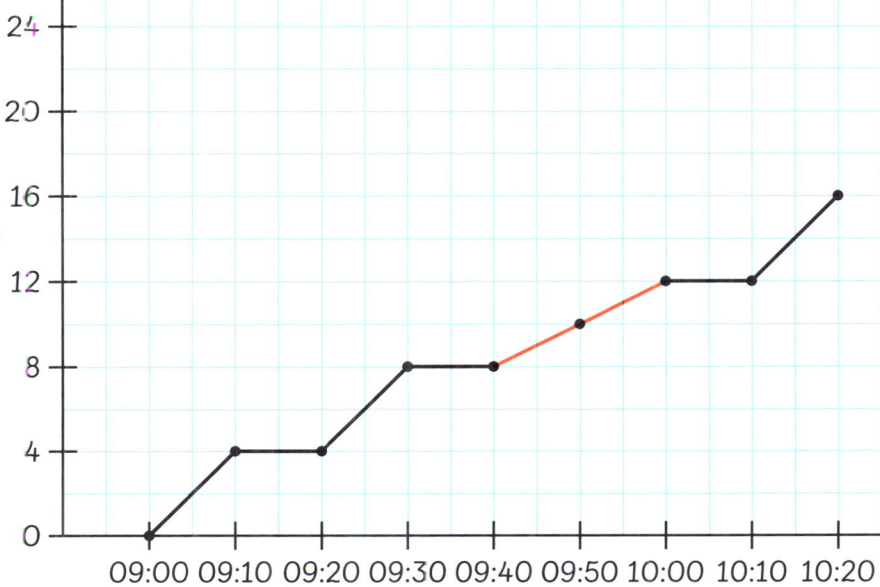

We can also find the start and finish times of the journey as well as the total distance travelled.

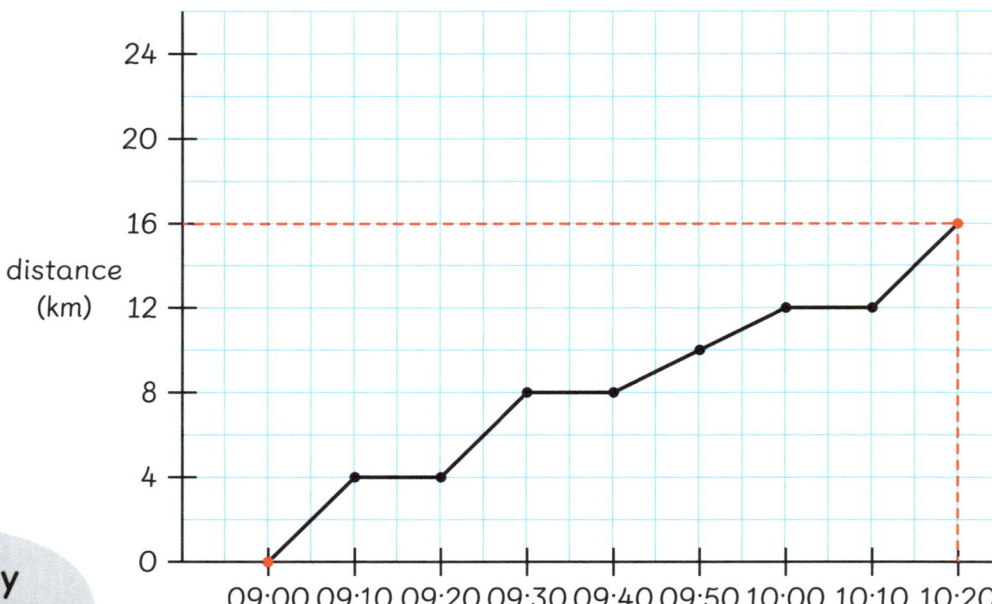

The bus journey started at 09:00 and finished at 10:20.

 The bus travelled 16 km.

Practice

1. The line graph shows the progress Holly made while reading her book last Sunday.

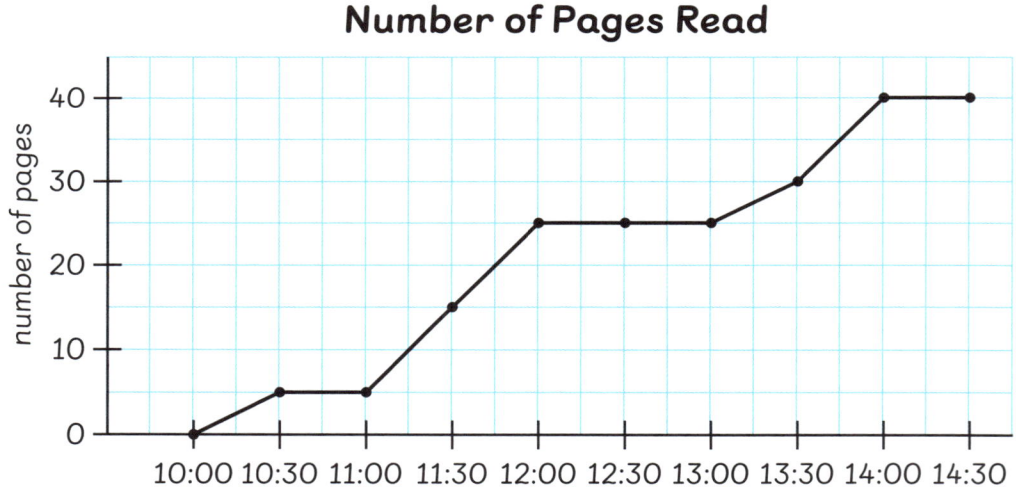

Number of Pages Read

(a) At what time did Holly start reading her book?

(b) Holly then read her book for 30 minutes before stopping to have her breakfast.
At what time did she start reading again after breakfast?

(c) Holly and her family started having lunch at 12:00.
Holly started reading again after lunch.
At what time did they finish their lunch?

(d) If Holly read at the same rate as she did between 13:00 and 13:30, how long would it take her to read 50 pages? ☐ h

(e) For how long was Holly reading between 10:30 and 13:30? ☐ h

2 Lulu and her mum painted their garden fence. The line graph shows the volume of paint they used over 4 hours.

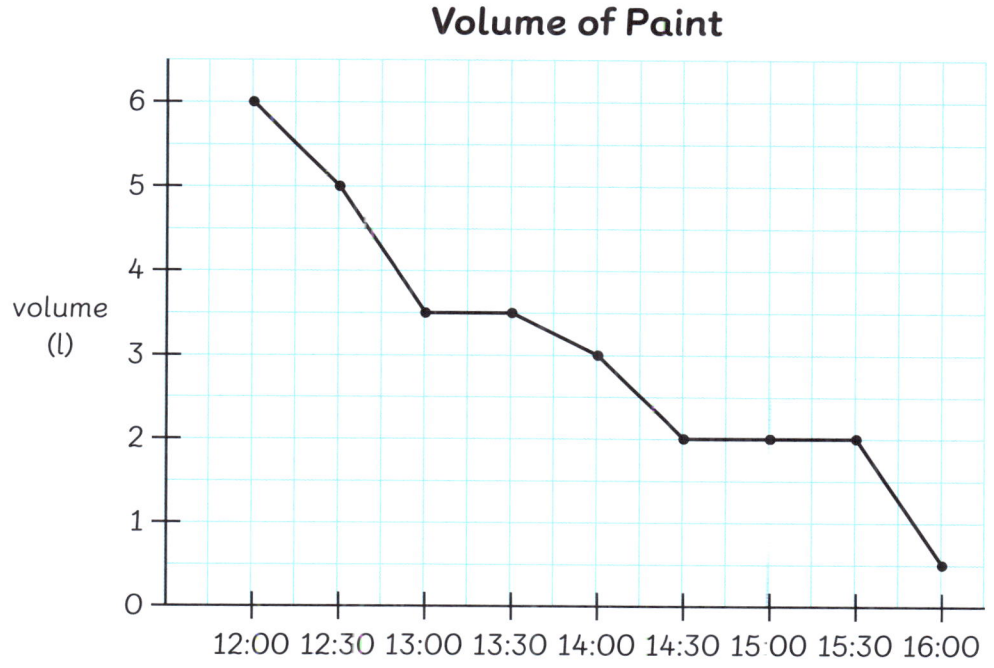

(a) Lulu started helping her mum paint at 12:30.
How much more paint did they use between 12:30 and 13:00 compared with the amount used between 12:00 and 12:30? ☐ l

(b) Lulu painted by herself between 13:30 and 14:00. The rate at which she used the paint when she was painting by herself was ☐ l every 30 minutes.

(c) From 12:00, it took ☐ hours to use 4 l of paint.

(d) Lulu and her mum stopped painting for an hour to have a late lunch. At what time did they start painting again after their lunch? ☐

33

Capacity

Lesson 14

Starter

Ravi wants to find the capacity of the large box.

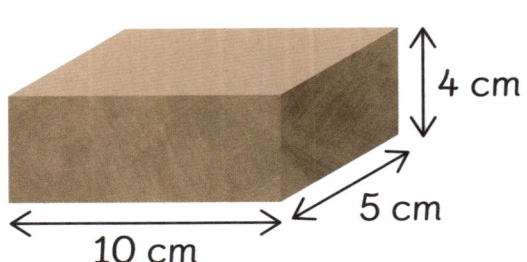

The length of the large box is twice the length of the small box.
The height of the large box is twice the height of the small box.
What is the capacity of the large box?

Example

Find the volume of the smaller box.

We can measure the capacity of the box using cubes.

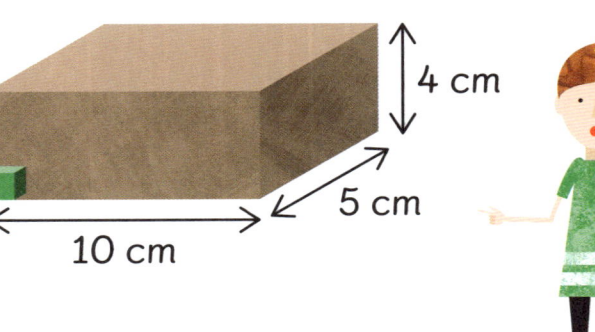

Each 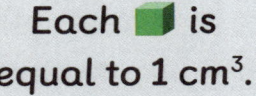 is equal to 1 cm³.

Each layer would have 50 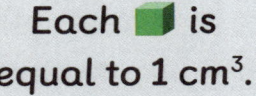.

10 × 5 × 4 = 50 × 4
= 200

The capacity of the small box is 200 cm³.

Find the capacity of the large box.

If one measurement doubles, the capacity also doubles.

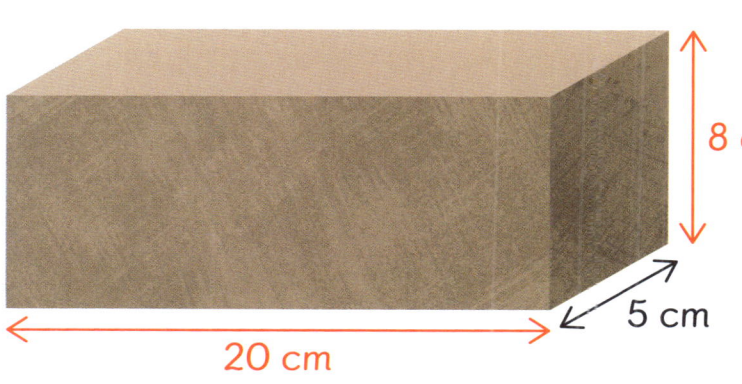

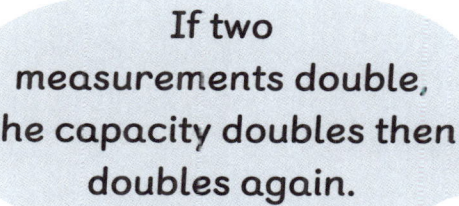

If two measurements double, the capacity doubles then doubles again.

20 × 5 × 8 = 100 × 8
        = 800

The capacity of the large box is 800 cm³.

Practice

Find the capacity of each box.

1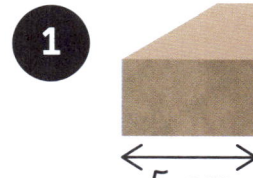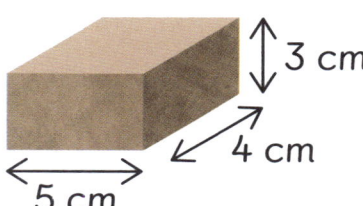

☐ × ☐ × ☐ = ☐ × ☐

= ☐

Capacity = ☐ cm³

2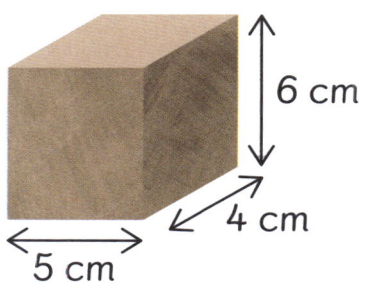

☐ × ☐ × ☐ = ☐ × ☐

= ☐

Capacity = ☐ cm³

Perimeter

Lesson 15

Starter

Jacob made this figure using 2 rectangles. Each rectangle is the same size.
What is the perimeter of the figure Jacob made?

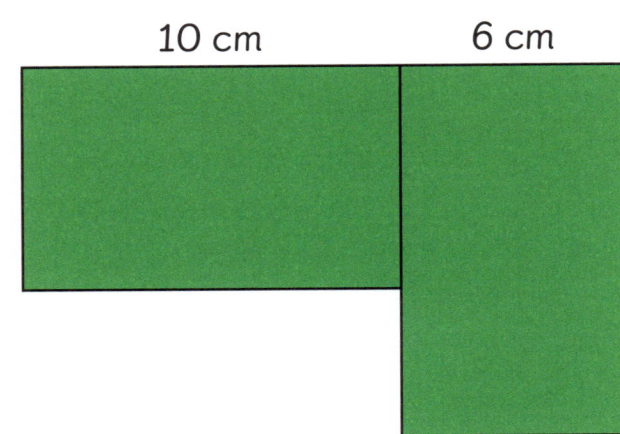

Example

I can label the sides I know.

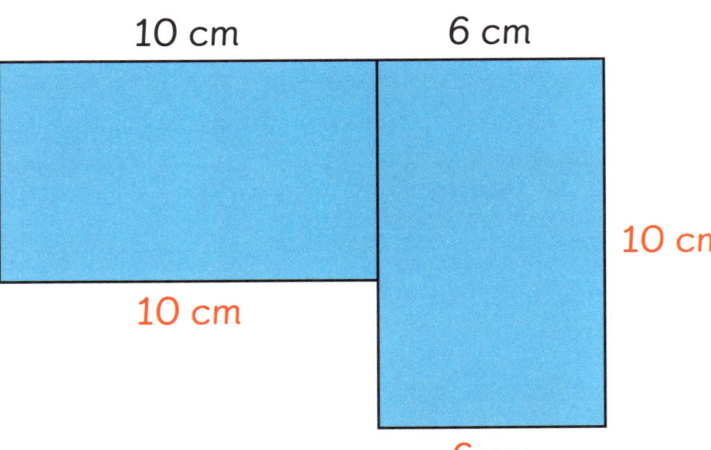

To find the missing measurement, I need to use the measurements I know.

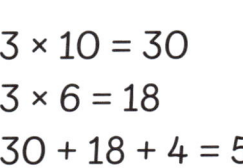

10 − 6 = 4

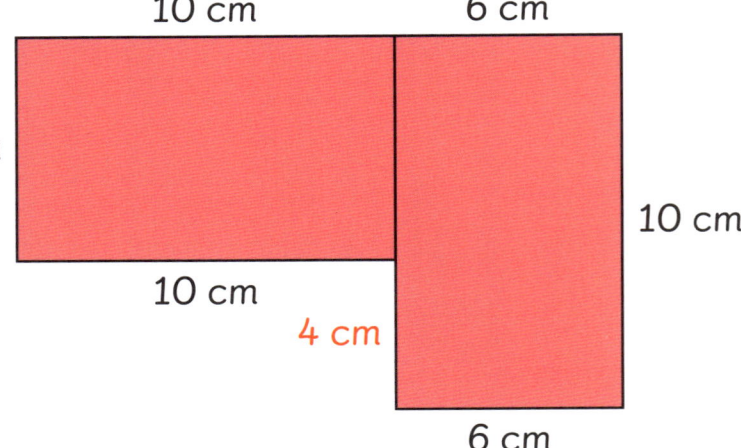

3 × 10 = 30
3 × 6 = 18
30 + 18 + 4 = 52

Perimeter = 52 cm

Practice

1 Find the perimeter of the following figure.
The figure is made from 5 identical squares.

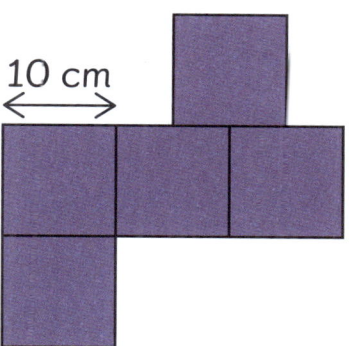

Perimeter = [ ] cm

2 The following figures were made using regular polygons.
The sides of a regular polygon are all the same length.
Find the perimeter of each figure.

(a)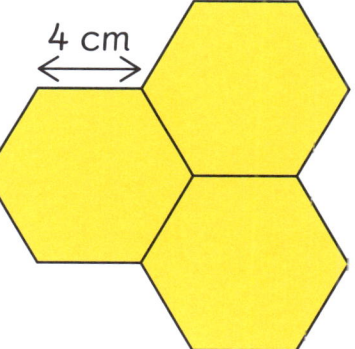

Perimeter = [ ] cm

(b)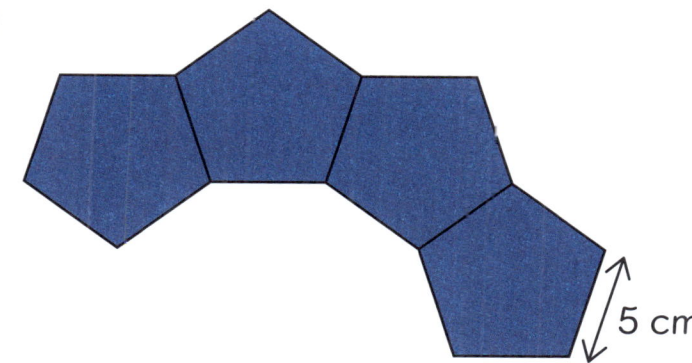

Perimeter = [ ] cm

(c)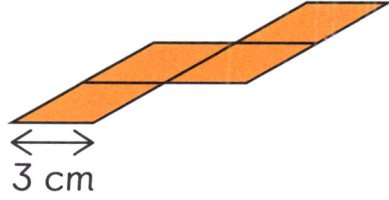

Perimeter = [ ] cm

(d)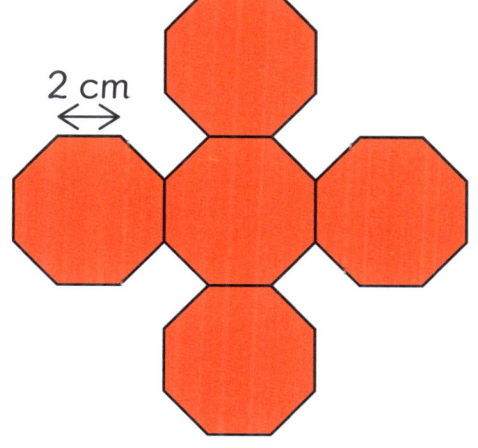

Perimeter = [ ] cm

37

Area

Starter

Hannah needs to find the area of her garden so she can buy the right amount of grass seed. How can Hannah find the area of her garden?

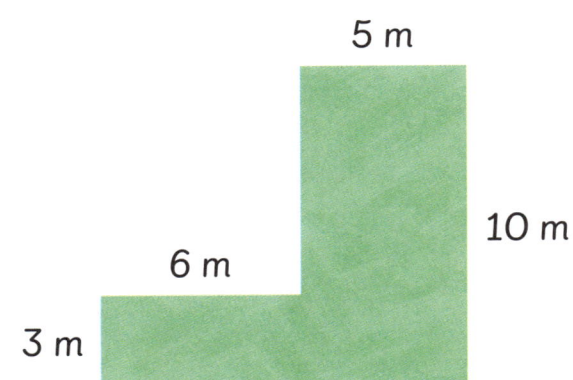

Lesson 16

Example

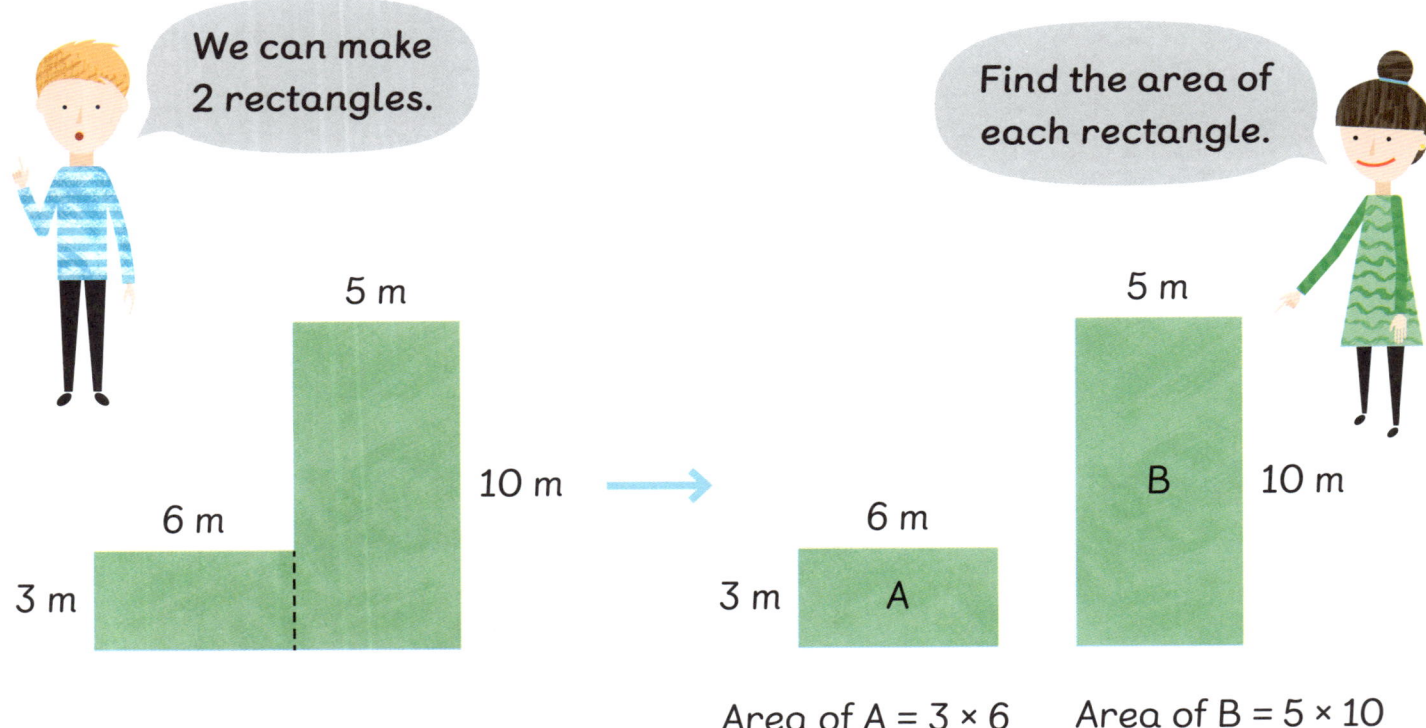

Area of A = 3 × 6
= 18 m²

Area of B = 5 × 10
= 50 m²

Area of A and B = 18 m² + 50 m²
= 68 m²

The area of Hannah's garden is 68 m².

Practice

Find the area of each garden.

1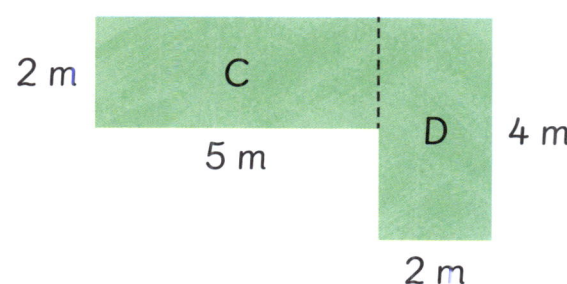

Area of C = ☐ × ☐   Area of D = ☐ × ☐

 = ☐ m²   = ☐ m²

☐ m² + ☐ m² = ☐ m²

Area = ☐ m²

2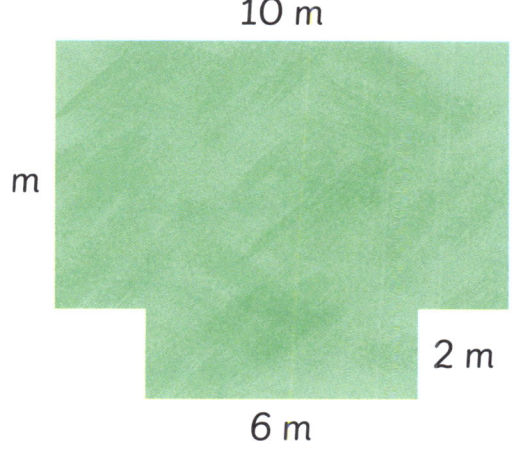

Area = ☐ m²

3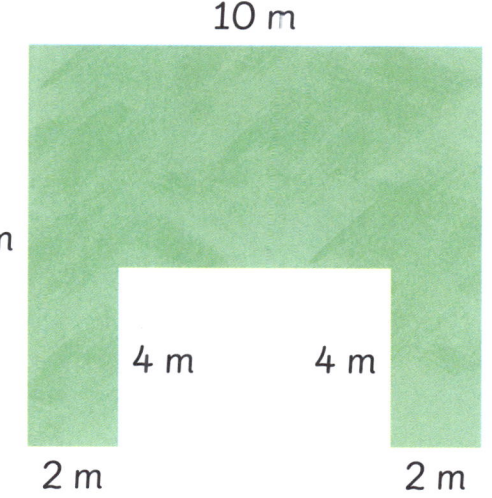

Area = ☐ m²

Angles

Lesson 17

Starter

Ruby drew a building using 2 identical rectangles.
She found the size of 1 angle but wanted to find the size of ∠s.

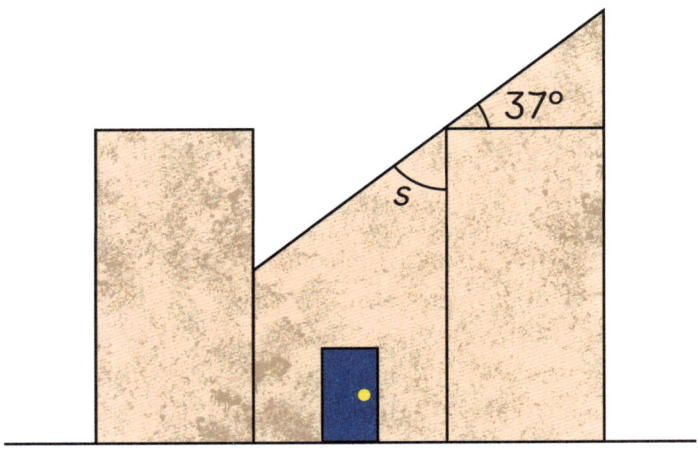

How can Ruby find the size of this angle?

Example

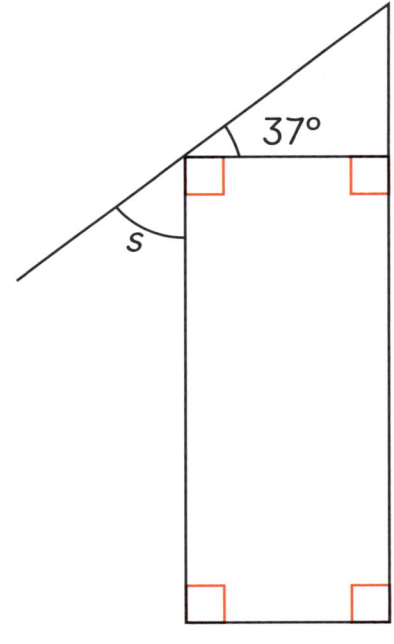

A rectangle has 4 right angles.

The 4 interior angles in a rectangle sum to 360°.

90° + 90° + 90° + 90° = 360°

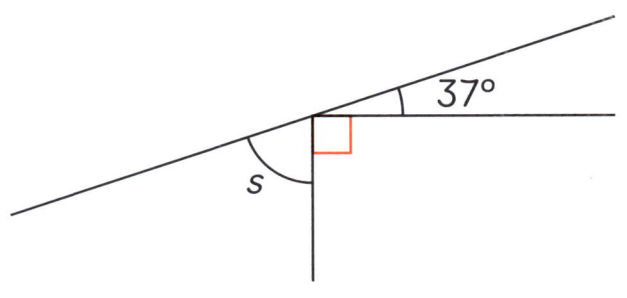

$s + 90° + 37° = 180°$
$s = 180° - 127°$
$s = 53°$
$53° + 90° + 37° = 180°$

$\angle s = 53°$

Find the size of $\angle m$ and $\angle n$.

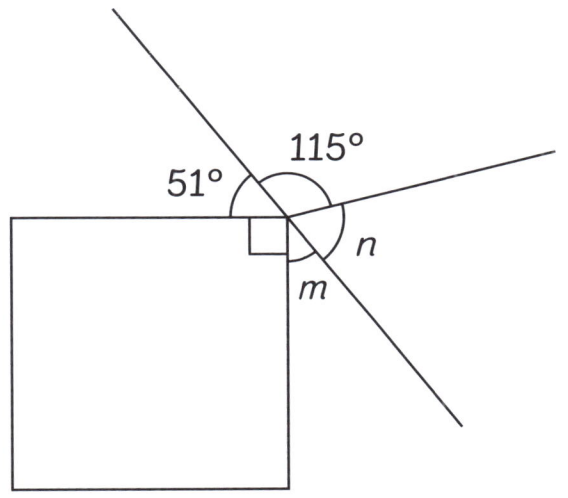

$51° + 90° = 141°$
$180° - 141° = 39°$

$\angle m = 39°$

Angles on a straight line sum to 180°.

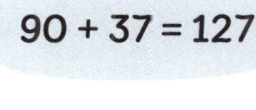

$90 + 37 = 127$

Start by finding $\angle m$.

51°, 90° and $\angle m$ are on a straight line.

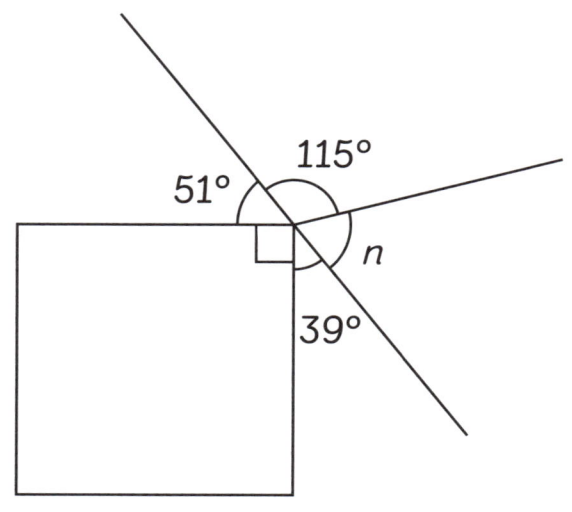

Angles at a point sum to 360°.

51° + 90° + 39° + 115° = 295°
360° − 295° = 65°

∠n = 65°

Practice

Find the size of each angle.

1

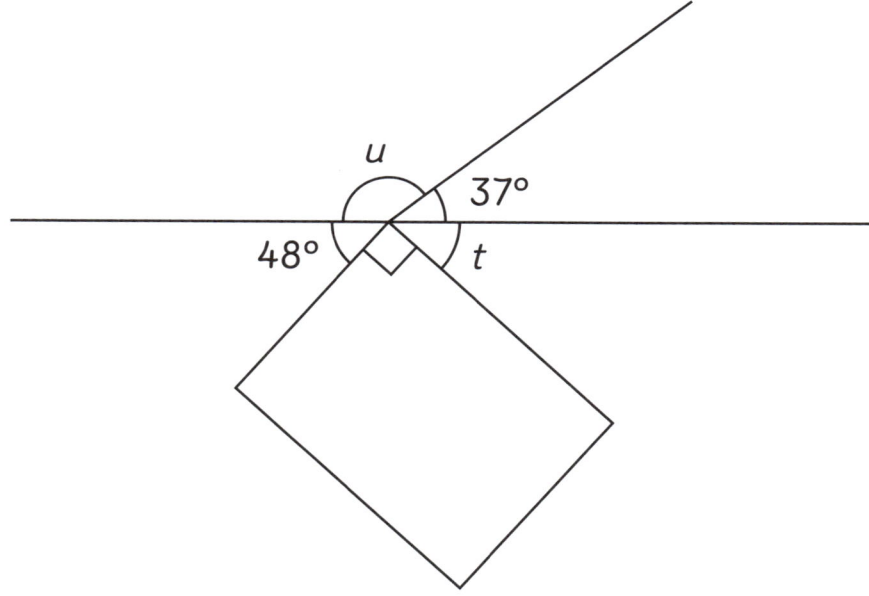

∠t = [   ]°

∠u = [   ]°

2

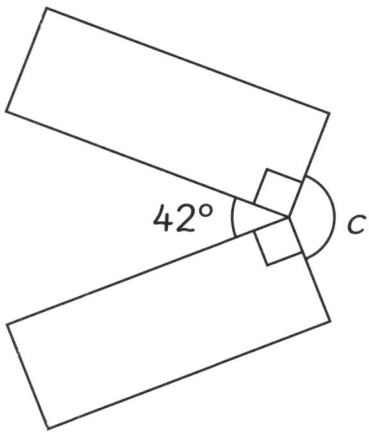

∠c = ☐°

3

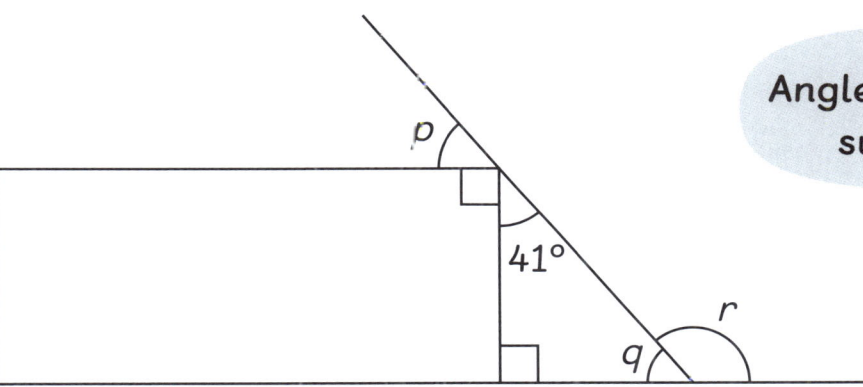

Angles in a triangle sum to 180°.

∠p = ☐°   ∠q = ☐°   ∠r = ☐°

Position

Lesson 18

Starter

Triangle CDE is reflected twice and is shown in its final position.
How has triangle CDE been reflected?
What are the final coordinates of triangle CDE?

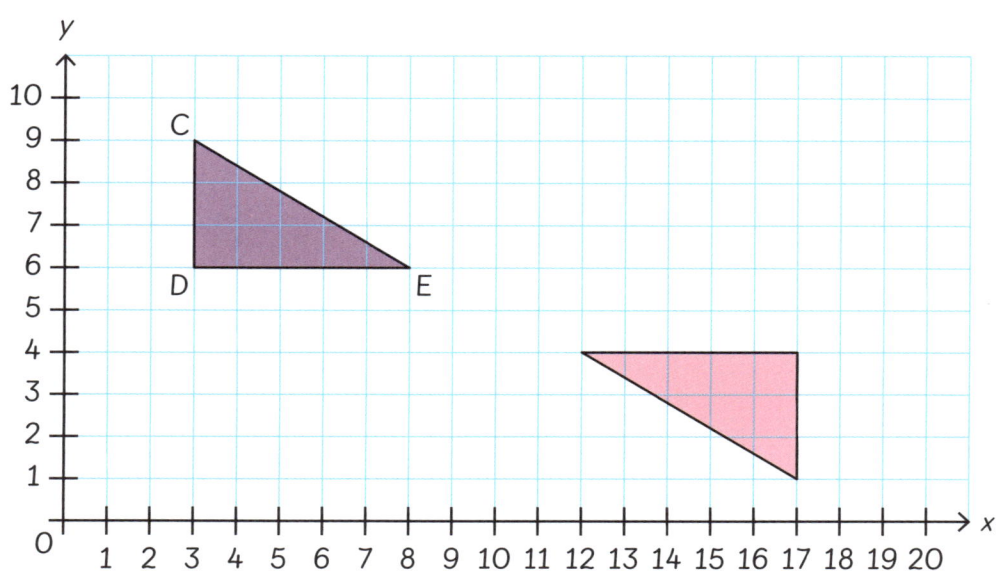

Example

The first reflection takes place in the line HI.

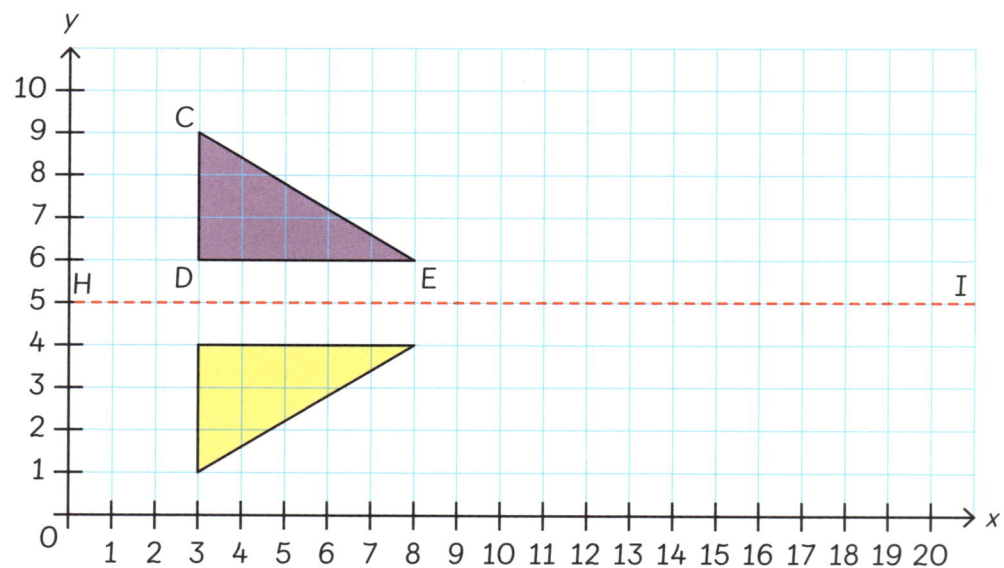

The second reflection takes place in the line JK.

C reflects from (3, 9) to (17, 1).

D reflects from (3, 6) to (17, 4).

E reflects from (8, 6) to (12, 4).

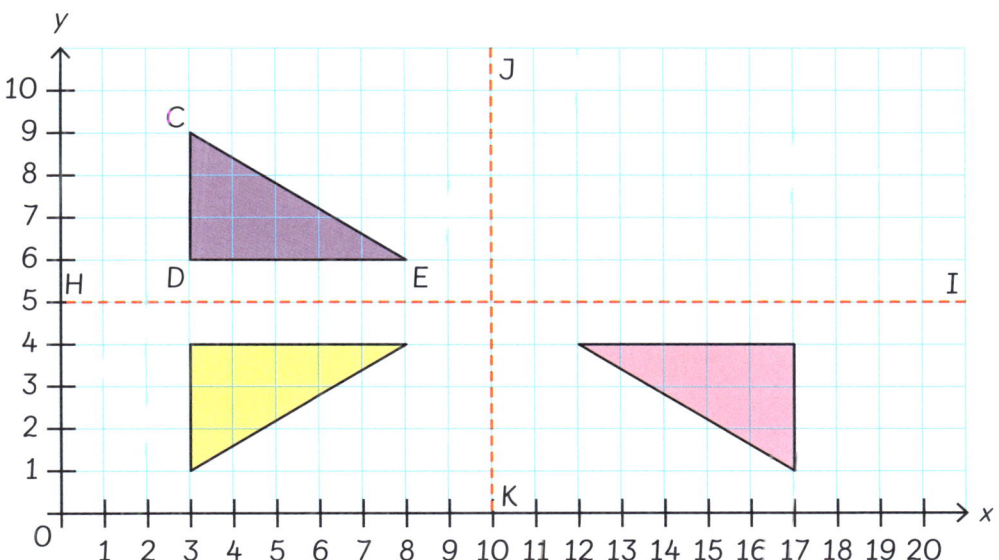

 We can find the coordinates of triangle CDE after the two reflections.

Practice

The trapezium JKLM is first reflected in the line CD. It is then reflected in the line EF. Draw the final position of trapezium JKLM to find the final coordinates.

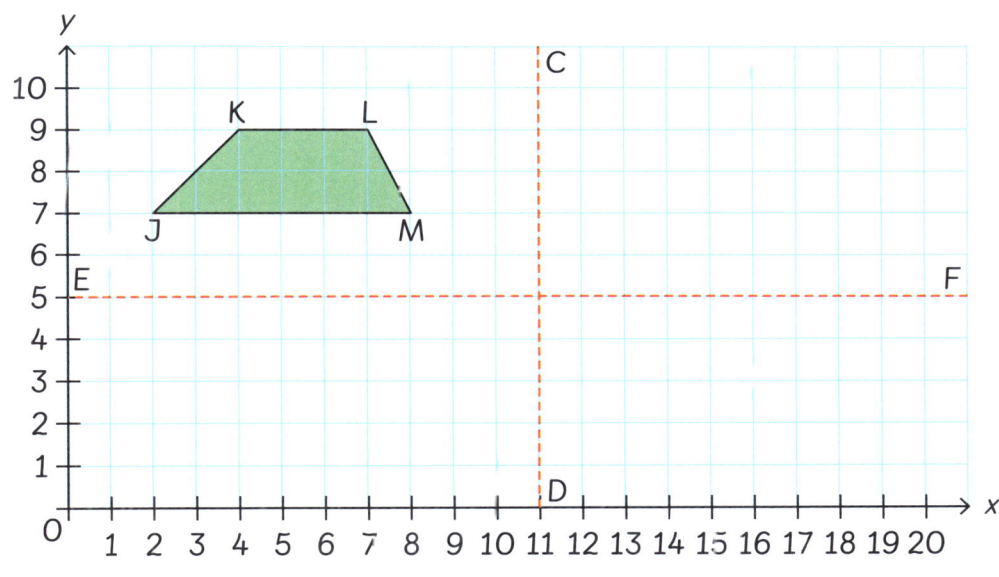

J reflects from (,) to (,).

K reflects from (,) to (,).

L reflects from (,) to (,).

M reflects from (,) to (,).

Answers

Page 5 1 (a) 508 243 (b) 497 325 (c) 473 201 (d) 512 799
2 (a) 223 357 (b) 352 237 (c) 522 337

Page 7 Emma's dad will have Rp179 996 left.

```
          820 004
  482 199        337 805

   ¹4  ¹5  ¹2  ¹1  ¹9   9              ⁹0̷  ⁹0  ⁹0  ⁹0  ⁹0  ¹⁰0
+   3   3   7   8   0   5       +       8   2   0   0   0   4
─────────────────────────       ─────────────────────────────
    8   2   0   0   0   4               1   7   9   9   9   6
```

Page 9 1 (a) 72 (b) The baker could pack the doughnuts into boxes of 12, 4 or 3 without having any left over.

Page 11 1

Composite numbers	Prime numbers
32, 14, 63, 15, 148, 117, 105, 144	29, 43, 101

2 75, 77, 81, 85, 87, 91, 93, 95, 99

Page 13 1

```
        ²2  ¹⁴3   5                    ²4   7   0       The products are the same.
    ×        2   8                ×         1   4
        ─────────────                  ─────────────
         1   8   8   0                  1   8   8   0
    +    4   7   0   0            +     4   7   0   0
        ─────────────                  ─────────────
         6   5   8   0                  6   5   8   0
```

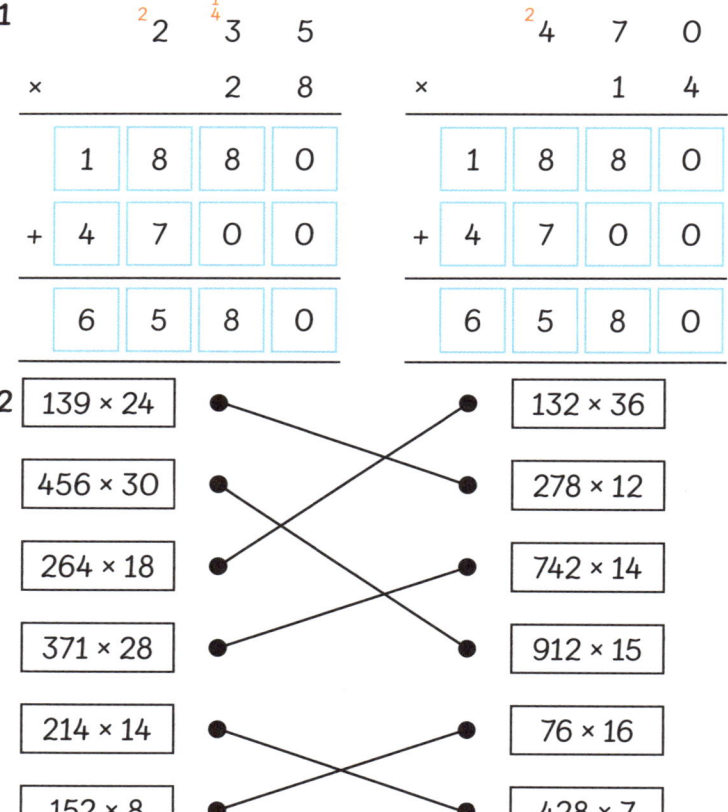

Page 15 1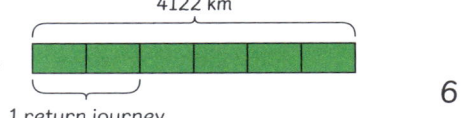

The distance between Plymouth and Newcastle is 687 km.

2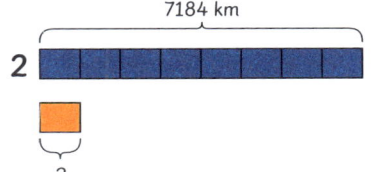

The distance between Paris and Genoa is 898 km.

Page 17 1 $\frac{1}{2} + \frac{1}{8} = \frac{4}{8} + \frac{1}{8} = \frac{5}{8}$; $\frac{5}{8} - \frac{1}{4} = \frac{5}{8} - \frac{2}{8} = \frac{3}{8}$. Ravi has $\frac{3}{8}$ l of paint left.

2 $\frac{3}{4} + \frac{1}{12} = \frac{9}{12} + \frac{1}{12} = \frac{10}{12}$; $\frac{10}{12} - \frac{1}{3} = \frac{10}{12} - \frac{4}{12} = \frac{6}{12} = \frac{1}{2}$. Ruby keeps $\frac{1}{2}$ l of the tropical punch for herself.

Page 19 1 $\frac{7}{8}$, $\frac{7}{8}$, $\frac{7}{8}$

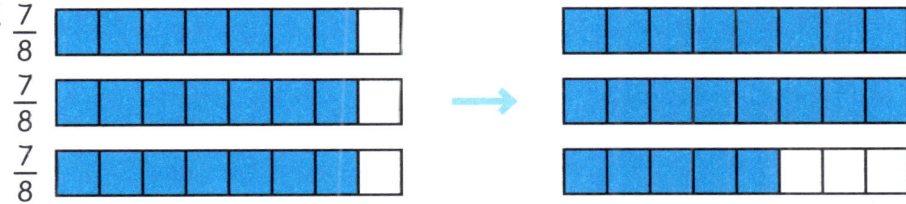

$3 \times \frac{7}{8} = 2\frac{5}{8}$. Oak has $2\frac{5}{8}$ chocolate bars left. 2 $4 \times \frac{7}{10} = 2\frac{8}{10}$. The total volume of soup Charles makes is $2\frac{8}{10}$ l.

Page 21 1 $2 \times 2 = 4$; $2 \times \frac{4}{5} = \frac{8}{5} = 1\frac{3}{5}$; $4 + 1\frac{3}{5} = 5\frac{3}{5}$. The restaurant has $5\frac{3}{5}$ cheesecakes.

2 (a) $3 \times 5\frac{5}{8} = 15\frac{15}{8} = 16\frac{7}{8}$. Sam uses $16\frac{7}{8}$ l of water to water the back garden.

(b) $3 + 16\frac{7}{8} = 19\frac{7}{8}$. Sam uses $19\frac{7}{8}$ l of water in total.

Page 23 1 (a) 3.44 > 3.05 (b) 4.99 < 5.01 (c) 2.564 < 2.645 (d) 34.014 > 34.01 (e) 5.679 > 5.08 (f) 6.1 > 6.099 2 (a) 3.4, 3.42, 3.5 (b) 9.08, 9.12, 9.131 (c) 13.001, 13.021, 13.101
3 4.35 kg, 4.307 kg, 4.039 kg

Page 27 1 (a) 2.34 kg + 2.155 kg = 4.495 kg. The total mass of the mixture is 4.495 kg.
(b) 4.495 kg − 1.7 kg = 2.795 kg. The mass of the remaining mixture is 2.795 kg.
2 Ruby has 9.95 m of thread.

Answers continued

Page 29

1

Team	Number of goals	Percentage of the total of 300 goals
Greystone Greats	30	10%
Hills United	75	25%
Plymouth Pirates	18	6%
Waterside United	60	20%
Tunbridge Tigers	57	19%
Brighton Bosses	39	13%
East Coast Flyers	21	7%

2 Charles: $\frac{10}{40} = \frac{1}{4} = \frac{25}{100} = 25\%$; Holly: $\frac{15}{25} = \frac{60}{100} = 60\%$; Ravi: $\frac{18}{30} = \frac{3}{5} = \frac{60}{100} = 60\%$;
Lulu: $\frac{49}{70} = \frac{7}{10} = \frac{70}{100} = 70\%$

Name	Maximum number of bonus points	Bonus points scored	Percentage of maximum bonus points scored
Charles	40	10	25%
Holly	25	15	60%
Ravi	30	18	60%
Lulu	70	49	70%

Page 32 **1 (a)** 10:00 **(b)** 11:00 **(c)** 13:00

Page 33 **(d)** 5 h **(e)** 1.5 h **2 (a)** 0.5 l. **(b)** The rate at which she used the paint when she was painting by herself was 0.5 l every 30 minutes. **(c)** From 12:00, it took 2.5 hours to use 4 l of paint. **(d)** 15:30

Page 35 **1** 5 × 4 × 3 = 20 × 3 = 60; Capacity = 60 cm³ **2** 5 × 4 × 6 = 20 × 6 = 120; Capacity = 120 cm³

Page 37 **1** Perimeter = 120 cm **2 (a)** Perimeter = 48 cm **(b)** Perimeter = 70 cm
(c) Perimeter = 30 cm **(d)** Perimeter = 64 cm

Page 39 **1** Area of C = 2 × 5 = 10 m²; Area of D = 2 × 4 = 8 m²; 10 m² + 8 m² = 18 m²; Area = 18 m²
2 Area = 72 m² **3** Area = 66 m²

Page 42 **1** ∠t = 42°, ∠u = 143°

Page 43 **2** ∠c = 138° **3** ∠p = 49°, ∠q = 49°, ∠r = 131°

Page 45

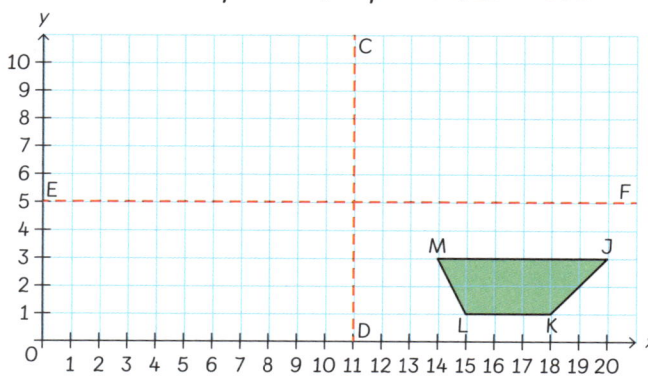

J reflects from (2, 7) to (20, 3). K reflects from (4, 9) to (18, 1). L reflects from (7, 9) to (15, 1). M reflects from (8, 7) to (14, 3).